easy-to-play duets for

flutes
or treble
recorders

Tunes for Two

easy-to-play duets for

flutes
or treble
recorders

thirty popular melodies
arranged by Christopher Tambling

Kevin
Mayhew

We hope you enjoy the music in *Tunes for Two* (Flute / Treble Recorder edition).
Further copies of this and the other books in the series
are available from your local music shop.

In case of difficulty, please contact the publisher direct:

The Sales Department
KEVIN MAYHEW LTD
Buxhall
Stowmarket
Suffolk IP14 3BW

Phone 01449 737978
Fax 01449 737834
E-mail info@kevinmayhewltd.com

Please ask for our complete catalogue of outstanding Instrumental Music.

First published in Great Britain in 1994 by Kevin Mayhew Ltd

© Copyright 1994 Kevin Mayhew Ltd

ISBN 0 86209 563 8
ISMN M 57004 520 4
Catalogue No: 3611118

5 6 7 8 9

All or part of these pieces have been arranged by Christopher Tambling
and are the copyright of Kevin Mayhew Ltd.

Cover Design by Jaquetta Sergeant
Music Editor: Anthea Smith
Music setting by Louise Hill

Printed and bound in Great Britain

Contents

For Nick Smith

Arranger's Note

Tunes for Two is a collection of thirty well-known pieces arranged as instrumental duets. These pieces can be used in a variety of different ways – they might serve as a useful introduction to ensemble playing; they could be used as sight-reading pieces during a music lesson; or they could be enjoyed simply as fun pieces at home or school. There is no distinction between 'pupil' and 'teacher' parts – players should feel free to swop lines!

The aim of this book is to provide duet material for players of approximately Grades 1 to 3 standard, starting with simpler pieces and progressing towards more challenging arrangements at the end of the book. I hope that *Tunes for Two* will be enjoyed by players of all ages and abilities.

CHRISTOPHER TAMBLING

TALLIS'S CANON

Thomas Tallis

WHEN THE SAINTS GO MARCHING IN

Spiritual

ALL THROUGH THE NIGHT

Traditional Welsh Melody

With fervour

WERE YOU THERE?

Spiritual

ODE TO JOY

Ludwig van Beethoven

Moderately

PASSION CHORALE

Hans Leo Hassler

Not too fast

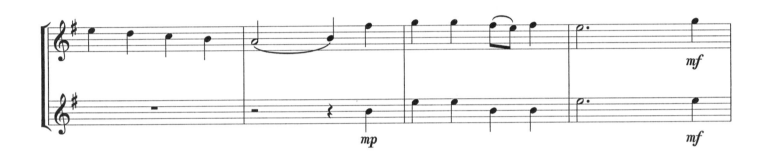

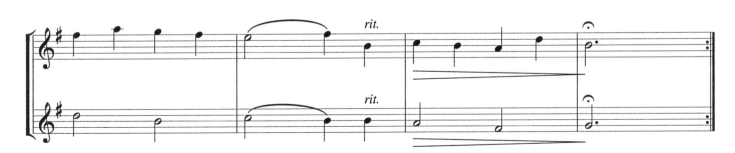

STEAL AWAY

Spiritual

ALL IN A GARDEN GREEN

Traditional English Melody

SPRING

Antonio Vivaldi

SKYE BOAT SONG

Traditional Scottish Melody

SOLDIERS' MARCH

Robert Schumann

BIST DU BEI MIR

Johann Sebastian Bach

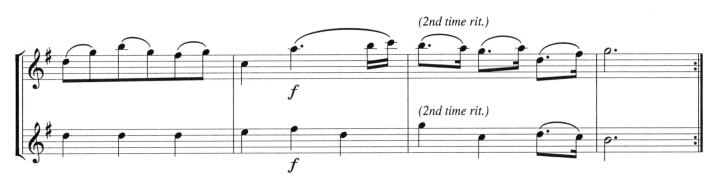

This arrangement © Copyright 1994 by Kevin Mayhew Ltd.
It is illegal to photocopy music.

BOURRÉE

George Frideric Handel

LARGO

Antonín Dvořák

PAVAN
16th Century Melody

MINUET

George Frideric Handel

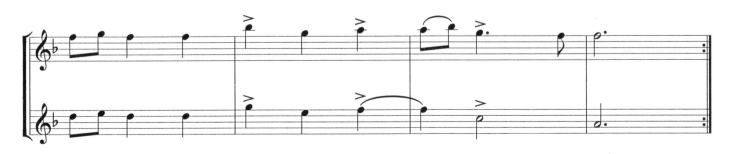

IMPROMPTU

Franz Schubert

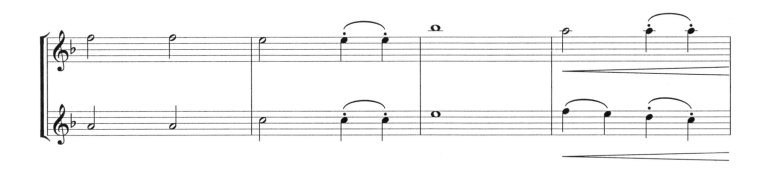

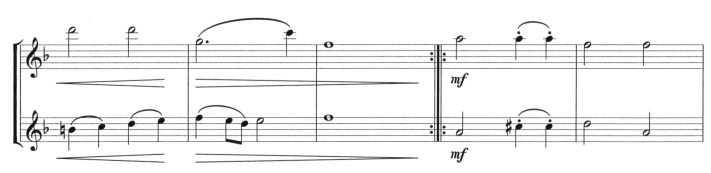

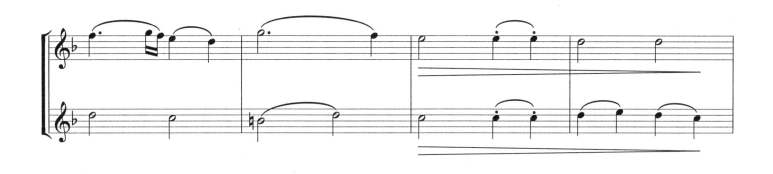

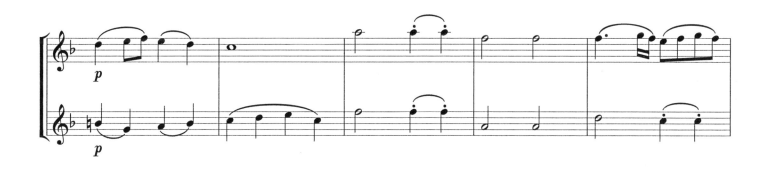

AUTUMN

Antonio Vivaldi

THE SILVER SWAN

Orlando Gibbons

MARCHE MILITAIRE

Franz Schubert

Con brio

30

MINUET

Wolfgang Amadeus Mozart

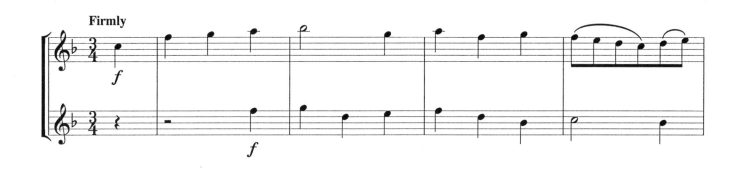

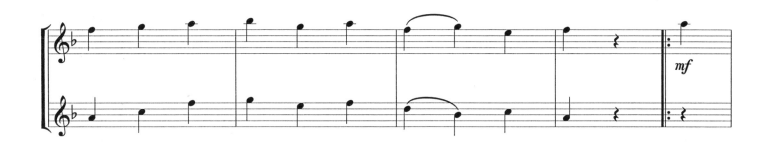

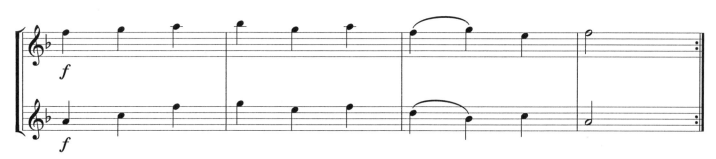

GREENSLEEVES

16th Century Melody

TRUMPET VOLUNTARY

Jeremiah Clarke

TO A WILD ROSE

Edward MacDowell

With simple tenderness

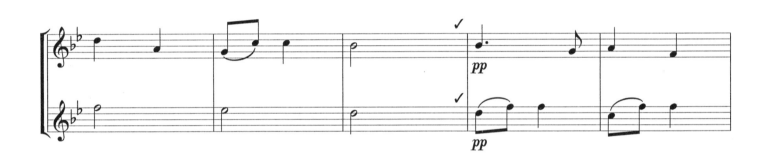

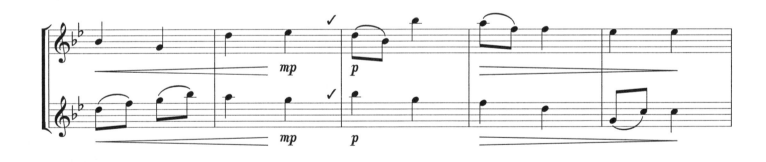

MARCH
George Frideric Handel

With vigour

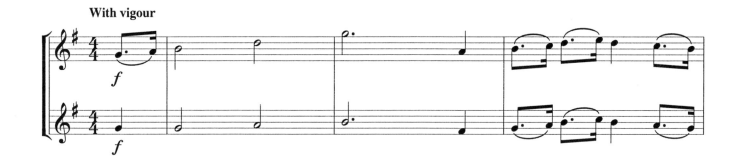

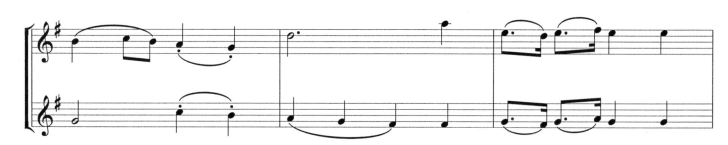

PAPAGENO'S ARIA
Wolfgang Amadeus Mozart

MY BONNY LASS SHE SMILETH

Thomas Morley

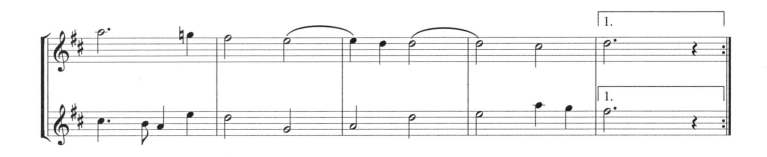

THE ENTERTAINER

Scott Joplin

7/30/02

NON PIÙ ANDRAI

Wolfgang Amadeus Mozart

COUNTRY GARDENS

Traditional English Melody

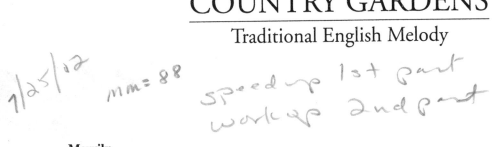

This arrangement © Copyright 1994 by Kevin Mayhew Ltd.

It is illegal to photocopy music.